ABCmouse.com
Early Learning Academy

Scissor Skills
and More

ABCmouse.com *Early Learning Academy* is the award-winning digital learning program that covers math, reading, science, social studies, art, music, and more for kids ages 2 to 8.

With more than 10,000 individual Learning Activities and over 850 lessons across 10 levels, ABCmouse is a proven educational resource that is trusted by parents and teachers across the U.S. and around the world.

Go to
www.ABCmouse.com
to learn more.

ABC Mouse

Visit **www.Walmart.com/Learning** for free learning resources to help you continue your child's education at home!

ABCmouse.com

At-Home
LEARNING TIPS ☑

Dear Families,

The keys to successfully managing a "learn-at-home" situation are often related to time and space. Here are a few tips to ensure that you and your child are getting the most of your opportunities to learn at home.

Managing Time

☐ Establish a routine for your day. For example, plan to start "learning time" at the same time every day, and schedule consistent breaks for meals, exercise, and free time. Make that routine as similar to your child's school day as possible.

☐ Set goals for how much time to spend on each learning activity, such as reading silently for 20 minutes. Be sure to celebrate when goals are achieved.

☐ Plan ahead for when you need time for yourself. Explain when that will be, and help your child use a clock to know when that time is over.

☐ Include your child in planning out how to spend your time. Children are much more likely to stick with a plan when they had a part in deciding what it is.

Managing Space

☐ Identify one or more "learning spaces" around your home. Pick places that are as comfortable and distraction-free as possible.

☐ Use headphones to cancel out noise when it's not possible to create a distraction-free space.

☐ Collect containers such as shoeboxes or small cubbies to hold school items.

☐ Choose one area of the house to store school items when not in use. Having a dedicated place to "turn in" and "pick up" items helps keep things organized.

☐ Allow children to use outdoor spaces when possible. Outdoor spaces provide fresh air and can help lift moods. They can also provide fantastic learning opportunities themselves!

☐ Just like with the last note about time, include your child in planning out how to use your space, too.

—Team ABCmouse

Things with Wheels

Cut on dashed lines. (✂----)

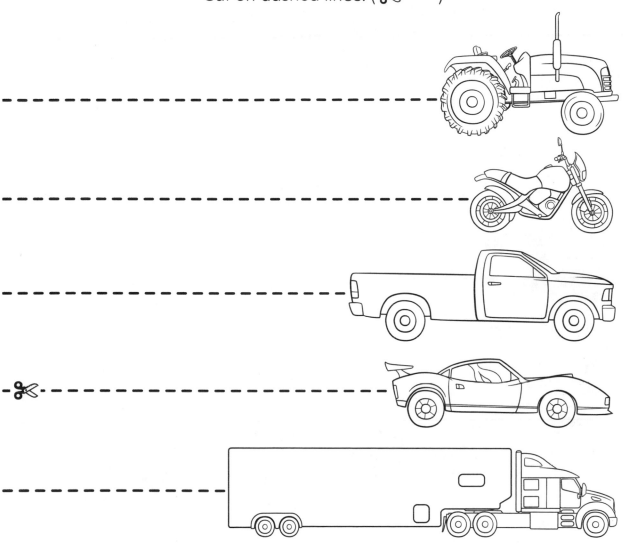

When cutting the dashed lines on this printable, be sure that your child is using safety scissors designed for young children and little hands. These scissors have round tips and blunt blades so that they will cut paper, but not fingers or other objects.

Shooting Stars

Cut on dashed lines. (✂----)

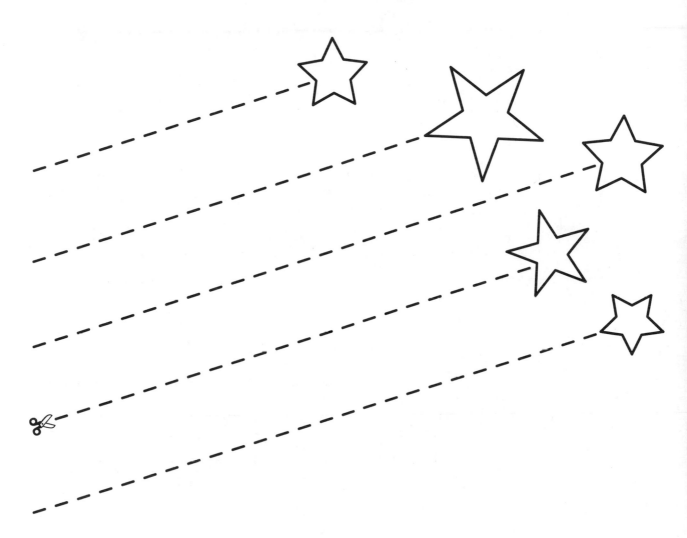

When cutting the dashed lines on this printable, be sure that your child is using safety scissors designed for young children and little hands. These scissors have round tips and blunt blades so that they will cut paper, but not fingers or other objects.

Envelope

Cut on dashed lines. (✂----)

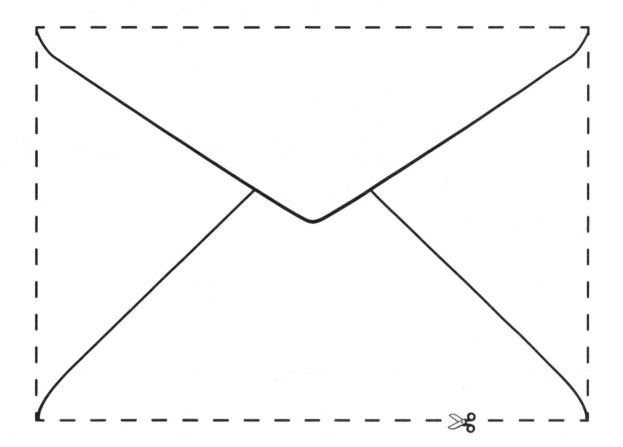

When cutting the dashed lines on this printable, be sure that your child is using safety scissors designed for young children and little hands. These scissors have round tips and blunt blades so that they will cut paper, but not fingers or other objects.

Farm Animals

Cut on dashed lines. (✂----)

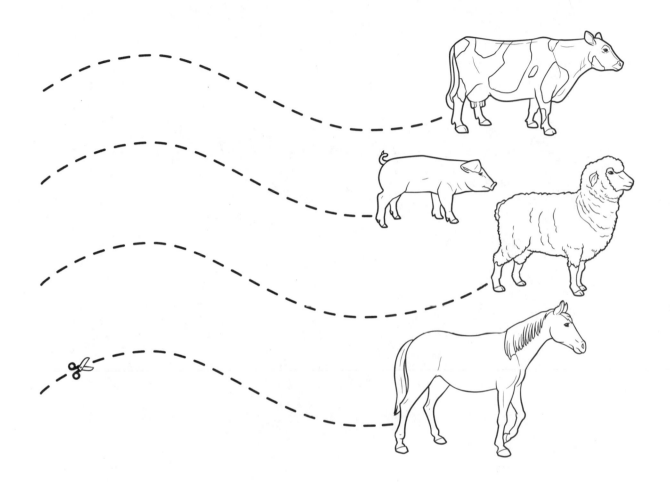

When cutting the dashed lines on this printable, be sure that your child is using safety scissors designed for young children and little hands. These scissors have round tips and blunt blades so that they will cut paper, but not fingers or other objects.

Beachball

Cut on dashed lines. (✂----)

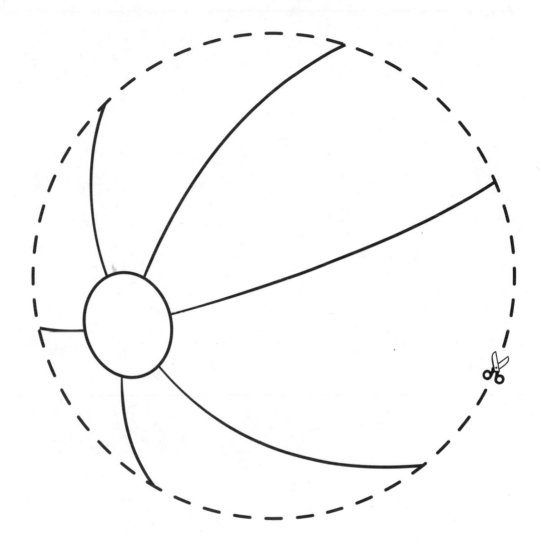

When cutting the dashed lines on this printable, be sure that your child is using safety scissors designed for young children and little hands. These scissors have round tips and blunt blades so that they will cut paper, but not fingers or other objects.

Paintbrushes

Cut on dashed lines. (✂ ----)

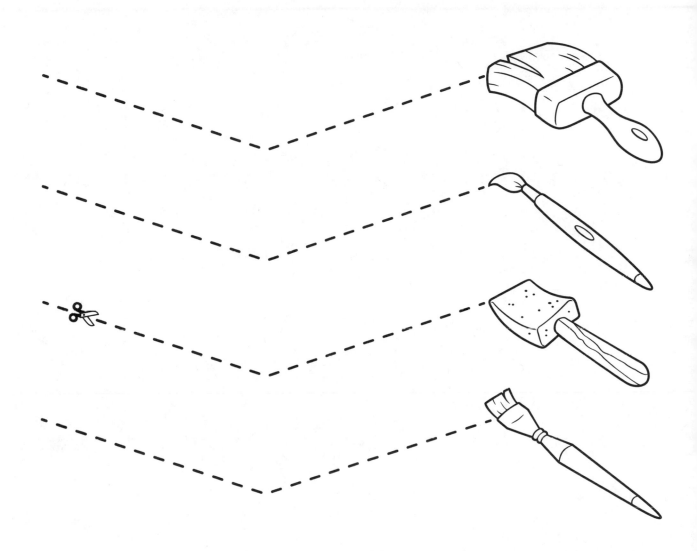

When cutting the dashed lines on this printable, be sure that your child is using safety scissors designed for young children and little hands. These scissors have round tips and blunt blades so that they will cut paper, but not fingers or other objects.

Crossing Sign

Cut on dashed lines. (✂ - - - -)

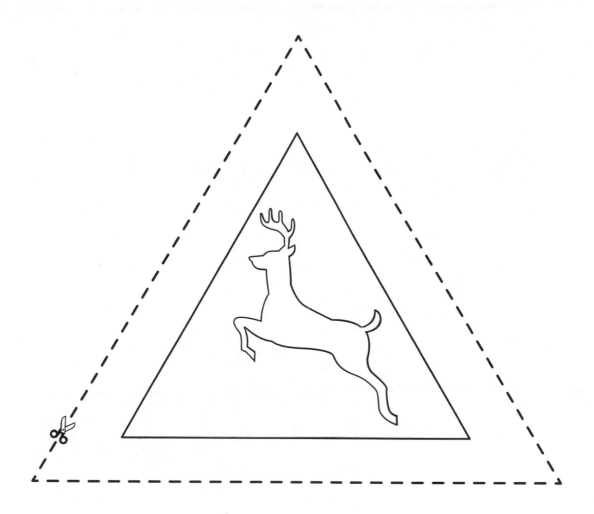

When cutting the dashed lines on this printable, be sure that your child is using safety scissors designed for young children and little hands. These scissors have round tips and blunt blades so that they will cut paper, but not fingers or other objects.

Porthole

Cut on dashed lines. (✂----)

When cutting the dashed lines on this printable, be sure that your child is using safety scissors designed for young children and little hands. These scissors have round tips and blunt blades so that they will cut paper, but not fingers or other objects.

Fire Trucks

Cut on dashed lines. (✂ - - - -)

When cutting the dashed lines on this printable, be sure that your child is using safety scissors designed for young children and little hands. These scissors have round tips and blunt blades so that they will cut paper, but not fingers or other objects.

Flag

Cut on dashed lines. (✂ - - - -)

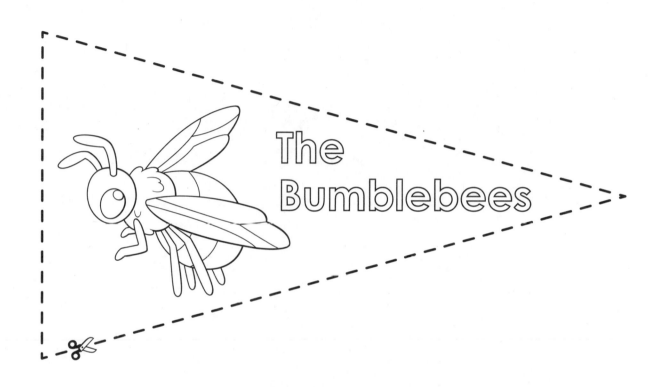

When cutting the dashed lines on this printable, be sure that your child is using safety scissors designed for young children and little hands. These scissors have round tips and blunt blades so that they will cut paper, but not fingers or other objects.

Clocks

Cut on dashed lines. (✂ - - - -)

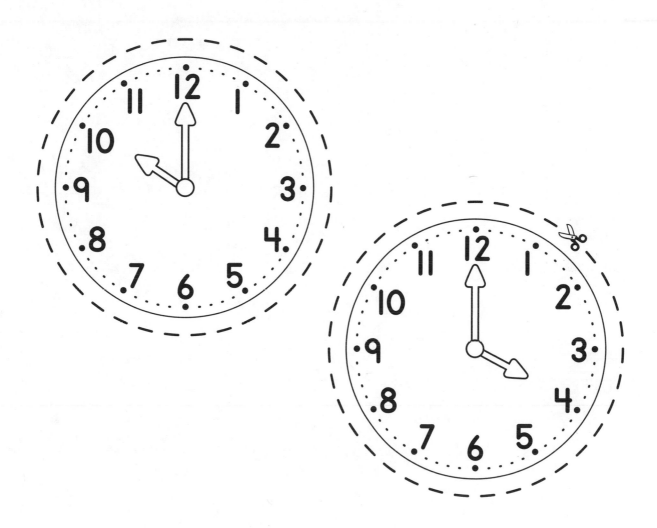

When cutting the dashed lines on this printable, be sure that your child is using safety scissors designed for young children and little hands. These scissors have round tips and blunt blades so that they will cut paper, but not fingers or other objects.

Fall Leaf

Cut on dashed lines. (✂----)

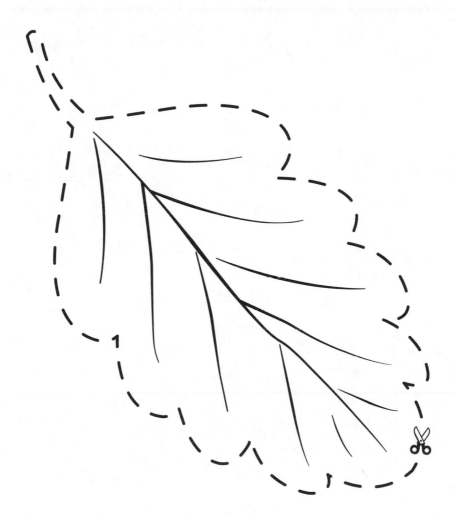

When cutting the dashed lines on this printable, be sure that your child is using safety scissors designed for young children and little hands. These scissors have round tips and blunt blades so that they will cut paper, but not fingers or other objects.

Play Ball

Cut on dashed lines. (✂----)

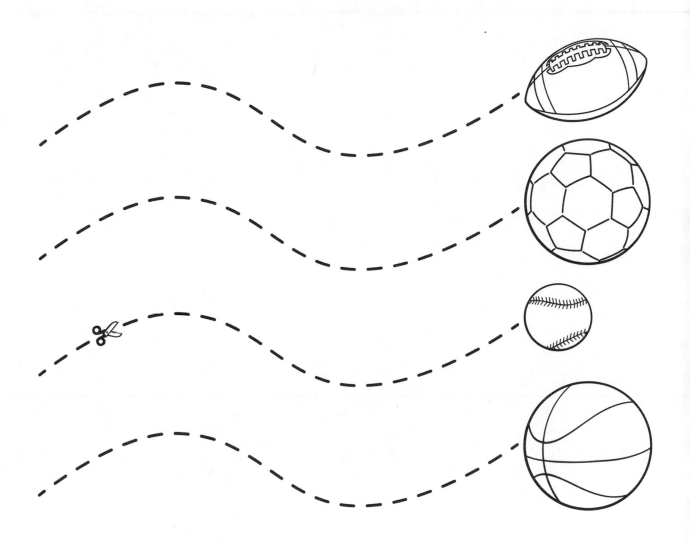

When cutting the dashed lines on this printable, be sure that your child is using safety scissors designed for young children and little hands. These scissors have round tips and blunt blades so that they will cut paper, but not fingers or other objects.

Cloud

Cut on dashed lines. (✁ - - - -)

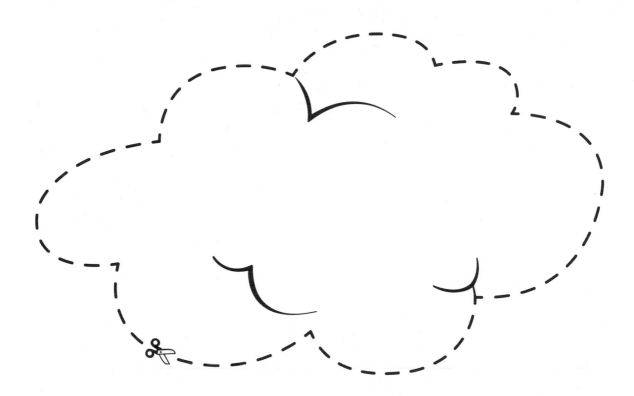

When cutting the dashed lines on this printable, be sure that your child is using safety scissors designed for young children and little hands. These scissors have round tips and blunt blades so that they will cut paper, but not fingers or other objects.

Candy Box

Cut on dashed lines. (✂----)

When cutting the dashed lines on this printable, be sure that your child is using safety scissors designed for young children and little hands. These scissors have round tips and blunt blades so that they will cut paper, but not fingers or other objects.

Owl

Cut on dashed lines. (✂----)

When cutting the dashed lines on this printable, be sure that your child is using safety scissors designed for young children and little hands. These scissors have round tips and blunt blades so that they will cut paper, but not fingers or other objects.

Windows

Cut on dashed lines. (✂- - - -)

When cutting the dashed lines on this printable, be sure that your child is using safety scissors designed for young children and little hands. These scissors have round tips and blunt blades so that they will cut paper, but not fingers or other objects.

Apple

Cut on dashed lines. (✂----)

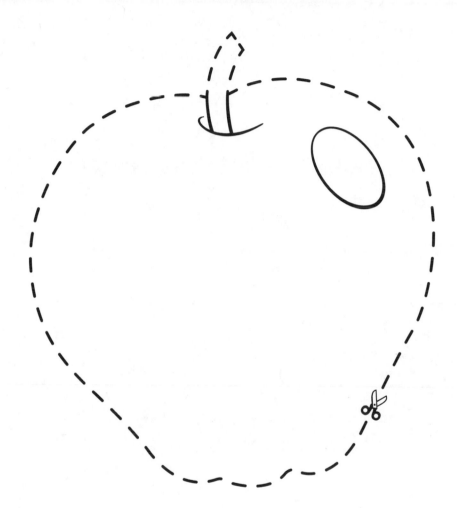

When cutting the dashed lines on this printable, be sure that your child is using safety scissors designed for young children and little hands. These scissors have round tips and blunt blades so that they will cut paper, but not fingers or other objects.

Zoo Animals

Cut on dashed lines. (✂----)

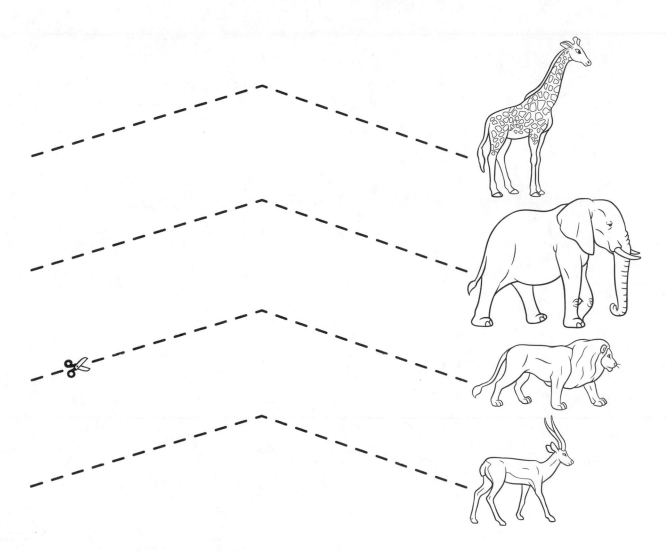

When cutting the dashed lines on this printable, be sure that your child is using safety scissors designed for young children and little hands. These scissors have round tips and blunt blades so that they will cut paper, but not fingers or other objects.

Kite

Cut on dashed lines. (✂ - - - -)

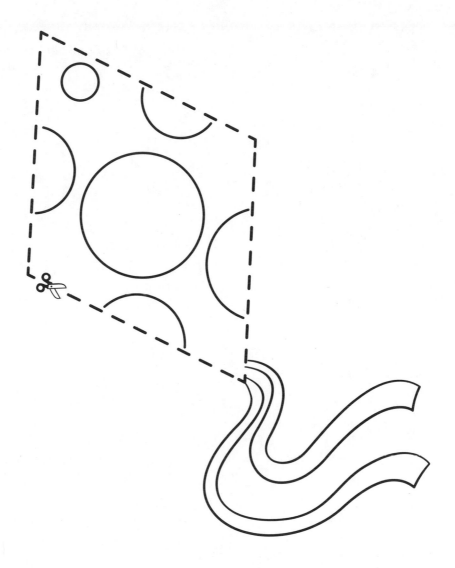

When cutting the dashed lines on this printable, be sure that your child is using safety scissors designed for young children and little hands. These scissors have round tips and blunt blades so that they will cut paper, but not fingers or other objects.

Our World

Cut on dashed lines. (✂----)

When cutting the dashed lines on this printable, be sure that your child is using safety scissors designed for young children and little hands. These scissors have round tips and blunt blades so that they will cut paper, but not fingers or other objects.

c

Fish

Cut on dashed lines. (✂ - - - -)

When cutting the dashed lines on this printable, be sure that your child is using safety scissors designed for young children and little hands. These scissors have round tips and blunt blades so that they will cut paper, but not fingers or other objects.

Fish

Cut on dashed lines. (✂----)

When cutting the dashed lines on this printable, be sure that your child is using safety scissors designed for young children and little hands. These scissors have round tips and blunt blades so that they will cut paper, but not fingers or other objects.

Coins

Cut on dashed lines. (✂----)

When cutting the dashed lines on this printable, be sure that your child is using safety scissors designed for young children and little hands. These scissors have round tips and blunt blades so that they will cut paper, but not fingers or other objects.

Street Sign

Cut on dashed lines. (✂ ----)

When cutting the dashed lines on this printable, be sure that your child is using safety scissors designed for young children and little hands. These scissors have round tips and blunt blades so that they will cut paper, but not fingers or other objects.

Tulips

Cut on dashed lines. (✂- - - -)

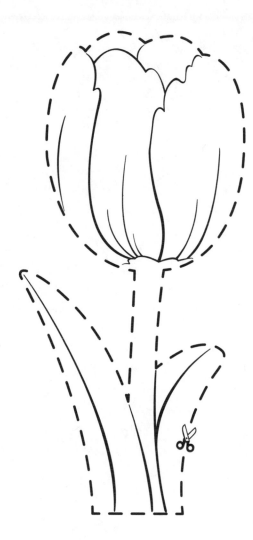

When cutting the dashed lines on this printable, be sure that your child is using safety scissors designed for young children and little hands. These scissors have round tips and blunt blades so that they will cut paper, but not fingers or other objects.

Things That Fly

Cut on dashed lines. (✂----)

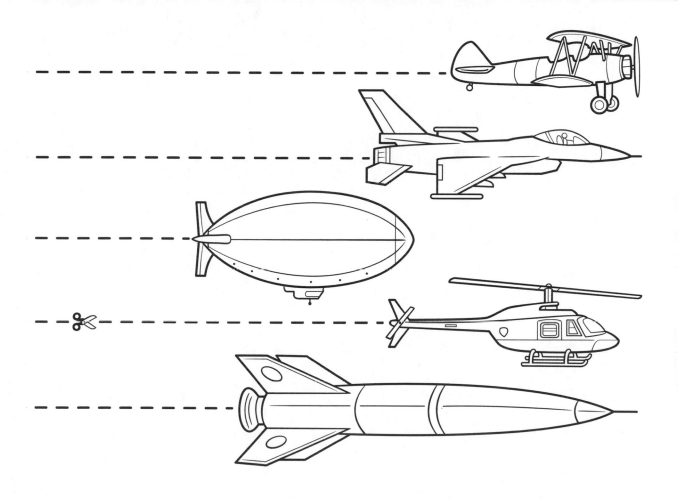

When cutting the dashed lines on this printable, be sure that your child is using safety scissors designed for young children and little hands. These scissors have round tips and blunt blades so that they will cut paper, but not fingers or other objects.

Rainbow

Cut on dashed lines. (✄----)

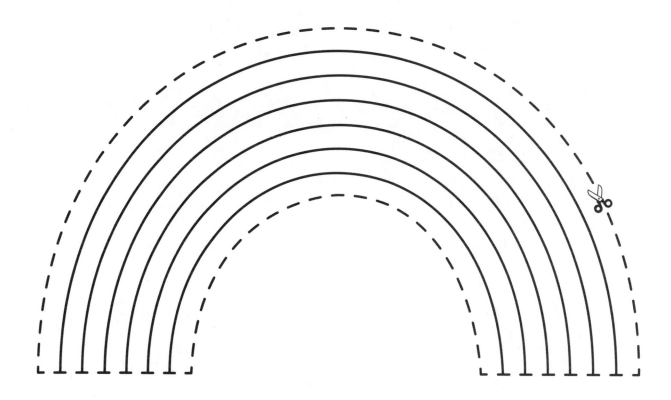

When cutting the dashed lines on this printable, be sure that your child is using safety scissors designed for young children and little hands. These scissors have round tips and blunt blades so that they will cut paper, but not fingers or other objects.

Sheriff's Badge

Cut on dashed lines. (✂----)

When cutting the dashed lines on this printable, be sure that your child is using safety scissors designed for young children and little hands. These scissors have round tips and blunt blades so that they will cut paper, but not fingers or other objects.

Fall Leaves

Cut on dashed lines. (✂-----)

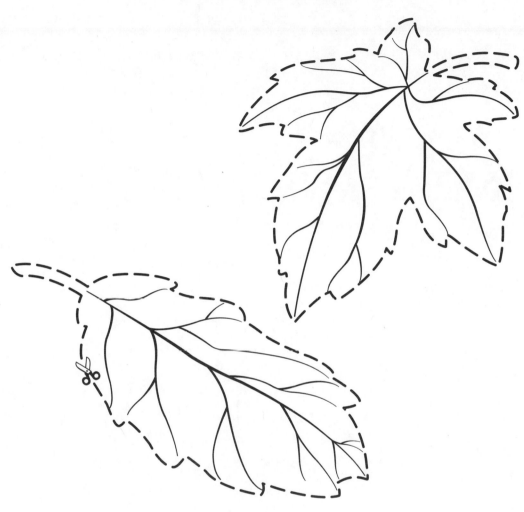

When cutting the dashed lines on this printable, be sure that your child is using safety scissors designed for young children and little hands. These scissors have round tips and blunt blades so that they will cut paper, but not fingers or other objects.

ABC Mouse Postcard

Cut on dashed lines. (✄----)

When cutting the dashed lines on this printable, be sure that your child is using safety scissors designed for young children and little hands. These scissors have round tips and blunt blades so that they will cut paper, but not fingers or other objects.

Make a Mammal Mask

1. Color the mask.
2. Ask an adult to help you cut out the mask and eye holes, and punch a hole on each side for string.
3. Tie the mask on and pretend you are a furry bear.

Make a Mammal Mask

1. Color the mask.
2. Ask an adult to help you cut out the mask and eye holes, and punch a hole on each side for string.
3. Tie the mask on and pretend you are a furry lion.

Color the shape below. Cut on the solid lines.
Fold on the dashed lines. Tape or glue the tabs.

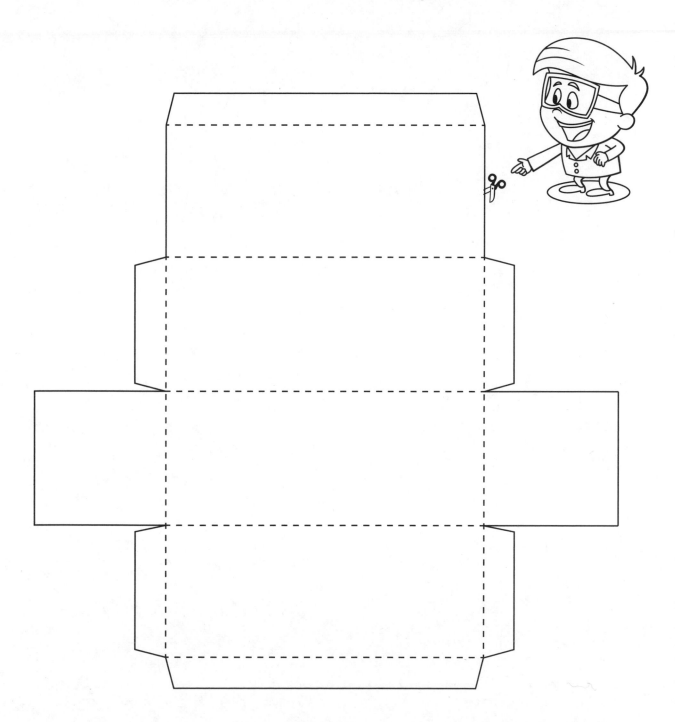

Color the shape below. Cut on the solid lines.
Fold on the dashed lines. Tape or glue the tabs.

Color the shape below. Cut on the solid lines.
Fold on the dashed lines. Tape or glue the tabs.

Color the shape below. Cut on the solid lines. Fold on the dashed lines.
Roll the rectangle into a tube, so line A meets line B. Tape or glue the tab.
Fold in the circles to cover the ends of the tube. Tape or glue the tabs.

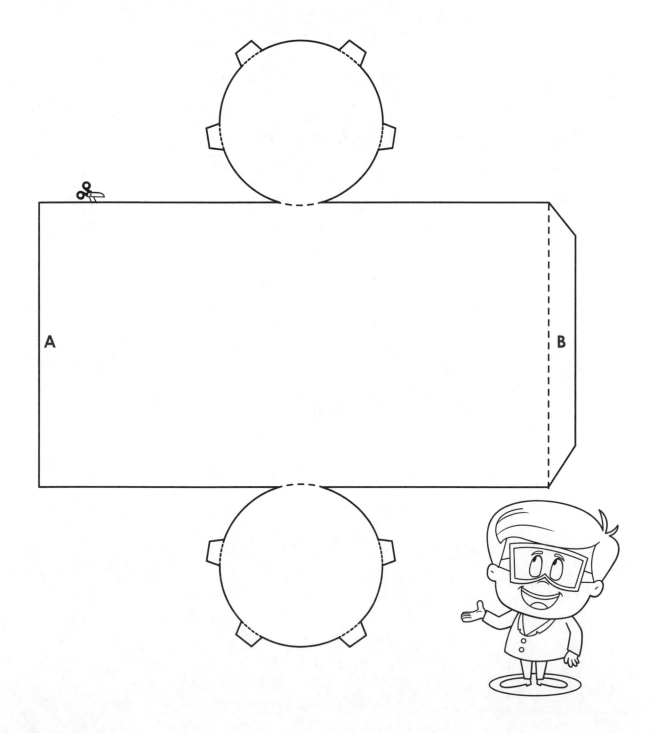

Color the shape below. Cut on the solid lines.
Fold on the dashed lines. Tape or glue the tabs.

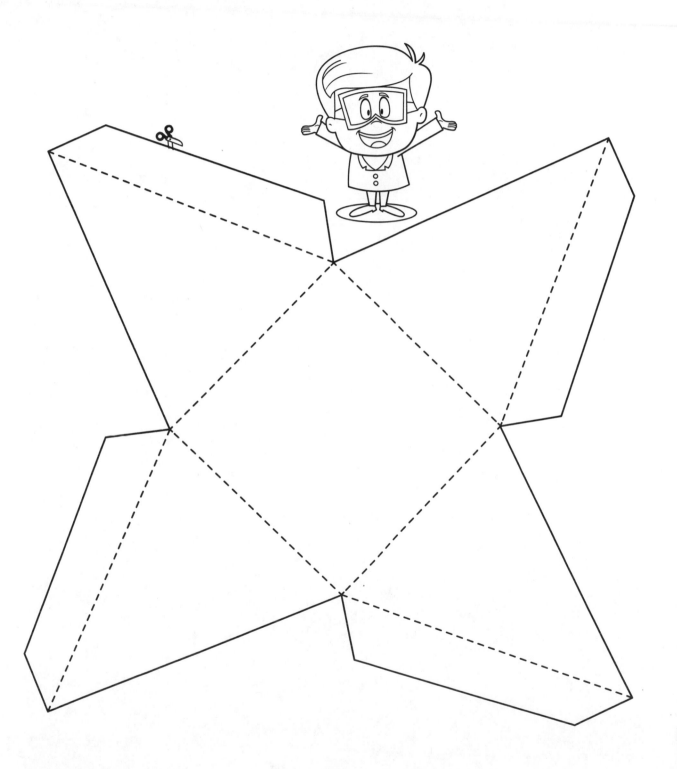

AWESOME!

Great!

WOW!

ABCmouse.com

ABC Mouse

Incredible!

Good job!

1·2·3 Mouse

Super job!

Nice going!

Do-Re-Mi Mouse

TERRIFIC!

Well done!

Very nice!

FANTASTIC!

You got it!

Yes!

AWESOME ★ JOB! ★

SUPER!

Good!

Way to go!

NICE JOB!

Great job!

WONDERFUL!

Excellent!